Travellers' Tales

WESTERN ISLES

GHOSTS WITCHES FOLKLORE LEGENDS
STRANGE MYSTERIES AND SECRETS

LANG SYNE
PUBLISHING

PUBLISHER'S NOTE

Stories in Part One are reprinted by permission of the copyright holders, from "The Lure of the Kelpie — Fairy and Folk Tales of the Highlands" by Helen Drever, first published by the Moray Press in 1943. Stories in Part Two are from "Selected Highland Folk Tales and Legends" and "More Highland Folk Tales" by R MacDonald Robertson, edited by Jeremy Bruce-Watt and published by Oliver and Boyd. This material is reprinted by permission of their successors, Longmans U.K. Part Three is taken from "Highland Smugglers, Superstitions and Second Sight" by Francis Thompson, published by Lang Syne in 1979.

This edition was published by Lang Syne Publishers Ltd, Unit 1C, Whitecrook Centre, 78 Whitecrook Street, Clydebank, G81 1QF and printed at the same address by Darnley Press. Original illustrations in Part Two are by John Mackay.

ISBN 185217 189 8

INTRODUCTION

What happened when the giant jumped over the Cuillins? How was a murderer literally caught red handed by his victim's bones? Where is the magic flag that can win battles for the soldiers who possess it? Who used rowan twigs and red thread to fight evil? Why is second sight a gift some island folk would rather be without?

These are just some of the questions answered in this fascinating journey through the legends and folklore of the Inner and Outer Hebrides. Many were taken down orally by the authors after being told for generations at ceilidhs around the peat fire flame.

Helen Drever's stc ies in Part One are written in a fairy tale style that will delight children of all ages! Discover what happened to the clan chief who angered the Black Dwarf of Jura. Discover where the fairies landed after being booted out of Heaven by God. Meet the Tiree manservant who was given a coat that made him invisible and shoes that allowed him to go about in absolute silence. We travel to Eigg for a special version of Snow White featuring a wicked Queen, a beautiful Princess and an all-knowing trout. And from Skye there is the tragic story of the mother who sold her soul to a witch doctor so her son could become a great musician.

If you like old legends, be they true, corrupted, or plain unbelievable, then the stories in Part Two by R MacDonald Robertson will capture your imagination. They were not originally intended to appear in print, but, as the author explained, "were written for the purpose of recalling to my mind, in after years, the scenes through which I have travelled and the stories that I gleaned.

"I have endeavoured accurately to collect first-hand information, and existing books have been avoided. I have also endeavoured to give a faithful description of people and places, avoiding exaggeration by which I might have rendered the work more attractive but less useful as a guide and encouragement to folklorists who may seek to follow in my footsteps."

His stories include: the ghost who frightened Macdonald clansmen out of their castle, the seer's prediction fulfilled when a dead man was shot by an arrow, the Harris woman ordered to bake for the fairies, the Clutching Hand doomed to float through eternity, Skye's huge sea serpent, the Benbecula mermaid given a Christian burial, and the secret that made a Skye family the greatest pipers alive.

He writes too of strange happenings and customs ... the people carried off by the spirit host, eerie noises in the night that signalled death in the household, a quaint cure for that withering optical beam, the Evil Eye, and the odd practice of throwing porridge into the sea in the hope of getting a better harvest. Then there are the Blue Men of the Minch .... who or what are thay and what does their appearance foretell?

And in Part Three the highly respected Stornoway writer Francis Thompson recounts island experiences of second sight and other extraordinary powers linked to the supernatural. He also explores the history of the various festivals and traditions that were the cornerstone of island life for generations, marking time through the various seasons of the year.

PART ONE

By Helen Drever

In this section we feature the enchanting stories from Miss Drever's "Fairy and Folk Tales of the Highlands" which she compiled from a rich variety of sources. "The Story of Puirt a Beul", "The Origin of the Fairies" and "The Origin of Music" were favourites at Skye ceilidhs for generations. The Highland variants of world famous tales were gleaned from conversations with islanders conducted more than 80 years ago. And John F Campbell's "Popular Tales of the West Highlands" proved an inexhaustible storehouse of legend.

The story of Puirt a Beul

From the seaboard of the Western Isles

Once in the Land under the Waves there lived a King who had a daughter of the rarest charm and beauty.

The King himself was beloved by the people of the Land under the Waves, but the love they bore to him was as nothing compared with the love they bore to the Princess, his daughter. She inspired the affection of noble and lowly alike, and her presence made a glow under the sea like the glow of the sun in the world above the waves.

Above all, everyone adored her wonderful singing voice,

whose music was far, far before the music that could be taken out of any instruments that were known there. And — strange though it may seem — there were musicians skilled in the use of instruments in the Land under the Waves; for the King and his Court were fond of dancing to music, and scarcely a night passed that they did not have a dance of some kind.

As was natural, suitors were not wanting for the hand of so charming a Princess, but she never showed any inclination to leave her father's Palace, until the Prince of Lochlann came to woo her.

And he not only wooed her, but before long he won her love and her hand; and when the day of the wedding was fixed there was both rejoicing and sorrow in the Court of the King of the Land under the Waves — rejoicing at the happiness of the Princess, but sorrow that she must go away and leave her people. And so they came to the wedding day — a day of glowing under-wave sunshine. That morning the Princess woke very early and said to herself:

"Why do I feel so happy? Oh yes, I remember! I am going to be married to my Prince this evening!"

And joy opened her lips and inspired her to sing for pure happiness. The tunes she sang had no words to them — they were tunes of the music that is known as Puirt a Beul — or Mouth Music. They woke all the echoes in the Land under the Waves and they woke all the courtiers, who began to dance, and kept on dancing. The very fishes began to leap in the water for joy, and even the birds in the world above the waves skimmed the surface of the waters — listening, listening to that joyous music. Then they soared away up into the sunshine, singing as if their throats would burst — for they, too, had heard the magic singing of Bheinn a Beul, the daughter of the King of the Land under the Waves. The echoes carried the music of her voice far, far away, and spread it as the ripples spread on the surface of a still pool into which a pebble has been dropped. They were heard on land and o'er sea, as well as in the Land under the Waves.

Away on the seaboard of Western Argyll there lived a fierce old giant named Fionn, who that morning was sitting by a loch, washing his feet, before starting off on a marauding expedition to the Isles. The echoes of that joyous sound stole to him from the Land under the Waves, and he lifted his head and listened. He grunted and growled to himself and pretended to be annoyed; but, in spite of himself, first one great foot began twitching in the water, keeping time to the music, then the other one kept it company. Then he rose up, and his whole body began to sway to and fro — and the waves rose high with his swaying and broke on the island shores. Then Fionn, the firece giant, danced, as no one — far less himself — had dreamed he could or would dance on this earth! Higher and higher he jumped, laughing and chuckling to himself, until one great leap took him over the Cuillins of Skye. And still the King's daughter kept on singing, and the more she sang the higher the giant leapt.

And now Fionn had leapt over the Cuillins of Rhum and landed in "*Cuin Siar*" (or the Western Sea) in a spot that to this day is called "the spot where Fionn washed his feet."

And still the King's daughter kept on singing for joy, and Fionn continued to dance; but now he was beginning to tire. Evening came on and he was still dancing feebly; but when night-time came, the great giant Fionn collapsed, and he lay down in the Western Sea and was drowned!

And there was great rejoicing all through the Isles of the Farther West, in the Island of Skye, and on the western seaboard of the mainland: and even in the Land under the Waves, for Fionn had harassed that region too.

And ever since then the Highlanders of the West have kept green the memory of the wonderful thing that the singing of the Princess of the Land under the Waves accomplished on her wedding day, when the great giant Fionn died of dancing to the mouth music of Bheinn a Beul.

The vengeance of the Black Elf of Jura

This is a story of "*Dubh Sith,*" the Black Elf of Jura, and Sir Lachlan Maclean of Duart.

Long ago there was always bitter strife and fighting among the clans of the Western Islands. From generation to generation, without ceasing, it went on. And in most of the fights were the Macdonalds — the descendants of the great Lord of the Isles — to be found. One of the clans which refused to be domineered over by the Macdonalds was the Clan Maclean, and bickering and fighting went on between these clans for long over a hundred years. At last matters came to white heat in a quarrel over lands in Islay, and the question was to be settled for ever in a great battle.

A day or two before the battle Sir Lachlan Maclean went to consult a famous witch about the prospects of his clan in the fight. The witch lived in a gloomy cavern — a terrible and awe-inspiring place it was — by the seashore, and Sir Lachlan — brave man though he was — felt that he would rather face rows and rows of Macdonalds than the eerie old crone who, muttering and crooning to herself, sat by a flickering fire at the back of the cave. As he approached her, he was greeted by a cackle of mocking laughter and the words:

"Well, Lachlan Maclean, so you have come to me?"

"You know me, mother?" said the startled chieftain.

"Know you!" said she. 'How then would I not be knowing you? I knew all your people, Lachlan Maclean; even your great-grandfather did I know — yes — and them that went before him. Two hundred years I have sat here, watching over the Islands and waiting, waiting, for peace to come — but it is not yet. No, it is not yet!" and her withered chin sank upon her breast.

"Well, mother, it is sad for my clan I am to hear that," said Sir Lachlan, "and I want your counsel. Tell me what is best to do to secure success in the fight that is coming."

"And how can I give counsel when I have nothing in my palm, Lachlan Maclean?" she said.

"Ah, but here is *gold,* mother, — plenty gold — to tickle your palm," said he, handing her a fat bag of coins.

Clutching it, the witch gave a shrill laugh of pleasure:

"That will warm my heart indeed, my son," she said. "I like gold. It is the only warm thing in the world except fire — for old age is cold, cold, Lachlan Maclean! Now see," she said, "for this I will tell you two things you are not to do, if you wish for success in the battle. The first is — you must not land on Islay on a Thursday. And the second is — no matter how thirsty you may be, you must not drink from the spring in Islay that is called 'Strange Neil's Well.' Avoid doing these two things, Lachlan Maclean, and all will be well with you. And maybe at last my old eyes will look upon peace in the Islands!"

The witch's advice seemed so easy to follow that the Chief looked upon the battle as already won, and well pleased he returned to his clan.

Now the very next day happened to be Thursday, so Sir Lachlan's plan was to land with his clansmen on the island next to Islay, and so be ready to attack the Macdonalds in Islay on the following day. Friday would be time enough, he thought, and so he would avoid the dangerous day.

Just before embarking, Sir Lachlan was accosted by a queer little dwarfy man who said:

"Sir Lachlan Maclean, I am Dubh Sith, the Black Elf of Jura, and I am coming to help your clan in the big battle in Islay," and he strutted importantly before the clansmen.

Sir Lachlan looked down at the tiny fellow and roared with laughter. "Ho, ho, ho," he said. "Oh dear me, do not make me laugh like this. It is not good for me! How could such a queer

The Dwarf accosted Sir Lachlan.

little dwarf help the great Clan Maclean? No, no! Away you and back to Jura and do not be making a laughing-stock of yourself."

This scornful treatment infuriated the Black Elf, and he went away, vowing that he would yet be avenged.

On Thursday morning, when the Macleans set sail, the weather was fine and fair, but suddenly a great gale sprang up, and fearing they would be wrecked, they ran for the nearest island. As they gained its shelter, Sir Lachlan said, "Now the good Lord be thanked, for this is the island we were making for, I am sure! But oh, it is thirsty I am after that battle with the stormy seas. In pity look for water for me!"

At that moment one of his clansmen said, "See, here is a fine spring. Come, my Chief, and you can drink your fill."

As Sir Lachlan slaked his thirst, a boy drew near and stared at the strangers.

"Ochanee!" he said, "Will you not be leaving any water *at all* in Strange Neil's Well?"

"What do you say?" said Sir Lachlan in horror. "Is this Strange Neil's Well? Then we must be on Islay!"

"And where else," said the boy, "but on Islay?"

"Alas! Alas!" said Sir Lachlan, "Is not that the evil luck indeed, after the witch's prophecy! What am I to do now?"

"Well," said the boy, "if you saw the Macdonalds that you are to fight, you would leave Islay this very minute. And they have the little Black Elf of Jura on their side too! He always brings luck."

"The Black Elf!" said Sir Lachlan in scorn. "What good could such a creature like yon do to anybody? I refused his help yesterday. Let the Macdonalds have him!"

For all that, the Chief was rather uneasy when he remembered how he had laughed at the poor dwarf; and indeed, as things turned out, he had reason to be uneasy.

Next day seemed bright and clear as the clans took up position for the fight. Uttering their war-cry, *"Beatha no Ba's"* ("Life or Death"), the Macleans rushed at the Macdonalds, whose war-cry of *"Fraoch Eilean"* ("The Heathery Isle") also filled the air. All Islay echoed with the clash of the broadswords and the whizz of the arrows from the bows of the archers. Now one clan would appear to be gaining ground, and now the other.

And through it all the Black Elf of Jura was watching, watching for a chance to take his vengeance on Sir Lachlan Maclean!

At last it came — when Sir Lachlan made for a little knoll from which to see the progress of the fight. Quick as lightning the Black Elf made for a high tree, and as easily as a monkey he climbed it. Where was Sir Lachlan now? Ah yes! There he was, on the top of the hillock. But what possible harm could the little Black Elf do to a man all encased in armour? He could watch, and wait — could the Black Elf — and presently he saw what he was looking for — an open joint in Sir Lachlan's armour! Then, carefully, an arrow was fitted to his bowstring, and carefully he took aim. Then — alas for Sir Lachlan Maclean! — the arrow whistled through the air and, penetrating the weak spot in the armour, Sir Lachlan Maclean fell dead on the spot.

And so the Black Elf took his vengeance! The Macdonalds drove the Macleans back to their boats on that day, and thus ended the terrible Battle of the Rhinns of Islay. And peace was not yet in the Islands!

The giant and the fair man-servant

A version of Jack the Giant Killer
From Tiree

Once upon a time the heir of the King of Erin shot a raven, and when he saw it lying dead on the snow he made a vow that he would seek all through the world for a maiden with hair like the raven's wing and cheeks like the raven's blood in the snow.

So he travelled east and west, and north and south, looking for this maiden. One day he saw a number of people going into a place like a church, at the door of which a dead man was lying; and he noticed with horror that the people just walked over the body. So he questioned a man as to why all the passers-by should do this terrible thing, and he was told:

"Well, this is the reason — he is a man who did not pay his debts, and he will be left to lie there until someone does it for him."

"Oh well," said the King's son, "be the sum large or small I will pay it rather than see what I have seen."

So the dead man was buried, and the Prince paid his debts and went on his travels again.

He began to get very tired; and while he was looking about for a place in which to rest he saw a woebegone creature approaching him — a red-haired youth, bareheaded and barefooted, who came and asked him:

"Do you want a man-servant?"

"Indeed, I haven't the means enough to keep a man-servant," the Prince said. "I'm only wandering about looking for the lady who is to be my wife."

"Well," the young man said, "I won't be the one who will ask much from you," and he pressed the Prince, who at last agreed to take him as his body-servant; and they went on their way together. Now, they found themselves approaching a large cave, and the man-servant said:

"A giant lives in that cave and no one gets past him alive, but if you do as I say we may be able to trick him. Stay you here and pretend you are putting an army through its drill, and make as much noise as you can — as if there were many with you — while I go into the cave."

When he got to the cave entrance, there was the giant, licking his lips.

"Ha! I'm glad you have come, for I'm *ravenous* for fresh meat!" he roared.

"Wait, wait! You needn't be in all this hurry," the man-servant said, "for the son of the King of Erin is out there with his army, and he has come to put an end to your life, Master Giant!"

And sure enough, when the giant looked out, there was the Prince at the corner, drilling away at men the giant supposed must be round the corner.

So he came back into his cave right quickly, and he said to the man-servant:

"Och! och! but you're right, and I like this not! But listen to me: I've two brothers far worse than me that you must encounter yet. Now, if you will hide me under this great stone I'll give you a magic quilt that will make you invisible, and you can escape my brothers that way."

"All right, then," the man-servant said, and he took the quilt from the giant, who lifted the great stone in the cave and got himself into the hole.

And the man-servant rolled the stone over and let it down edgeways on the giant so that it ground him to powder!

Then he and the Prince filled their pockets with treasure that was in the cave and went on their way.

They soon came to great rocks and precipices, and the man-servant told the Prince that there was another and bigger giant among those great rocks; and that he'd better do as before, and pretend to be drilling troops. And while the Prince was at his shouting and ordering, the man-servant went on among the rocks and saw the second giant parading up and down.

"Ha, you have come!" he said. "I am without food, and I'm right glad to see you! You will at least make my dinner, and you might even make my supper as well; so I'll just go and sharpen my knife!"

"Have me or want me," said the fair man-servant, "but indeed it would be better for you to look out and see what you can see — the son of the King of Erin drilling the troops he has brought to capture and kill you!"

Out rushed the giant, and he saw the young man drilling

away with a great noise, at troops he supposed were just around the corner — and back he came in great trouble of mind.

"What am I to do, and where am I to hide?" he said.

"Well," the fair man-servant said, "I hid your brother yesterday, and he gave me an invisible quilt as a reward. Now what will you give me if I advise you also?"

"I will give you a pair of shoes of quietness," the giant said, "and when you put them on no one will know you are walking near them at all. But if I do, will you promise to let me down to the foot of this precipice out of sight of the Prince and his army?"

The man-servant agreed, and he took the shoes of quietness; then he put a chain around the giant's middle and began to let him down the precipice. And when he was just nearing the bottom he let the chain go, and the giant was dashed to pieces at the bottom of the rocks!

And then the Prince and the man-servant went to the giant's house and helped themselves to quantities of gold and silver and jewels before they went again on their travels.

And the road was smooth before them until they reached the place where the last and greatest giant lived. In front of it were five spikes, on four of which were the heads of people the giant had killed.

A beautiful maiden came out of the house to meet them, and whenever he saw her the Prince knew that this was she whom he was seeking — the maiden with hair like the raven's wing and cheeks like the raven's blood on the snow; and his heart was singing for joy! In her hand was a spoon, and she told the Prince that he was going to be put to a test, and if he couldn't meet the giant with that spoon in his hand to-morrow morning at sunrise, then his head would occupy the fifth spike!

"Then just give me the spoon," said the Prince.

"No, no," she said, that is not the way the giant will have it. He would kill me if I did that!" And she went away to the seashore by herself and buried the spoon deep down among the sand. And the giant chuckled and laughed, for, said he:

"The sands of the seashore are miles long and miles wide, and who will know where to dig?"

But the man-servant had put on his invisible quilt and his shoes of quietness, and had gone behind the maiden; so when she had gone away from the spot where the spoon was buried he just dug it up again and took it to the Prince.

And oh! the rage of the giant when the Prince met him at sunrise with the spoon in his hand!

He sulked all day, and at evening he thought of another test; and he took out a silver comb from the maiden's hair and said to the Prince:

"Unless you can replace that comb in the maiden's hair at sunrise your head will be on the fifth spike," and he went away to the shore to bury the comb himself this time.

Again the man-servant donned the invisible quilt and the shoes of quietness, and followed unseen and unheard; and again he dug where the giant had buried the comb and took it to the Prince. And when the Prince replaced the comb in the maiden's hair at sunrise the giant foamed at the mouth in his rage!

Then came the third night, and the Prince said to the maiden:

"Why will you be waiting on here with the giant? Come away with me and we will be married."

But she said with a sigh:

"No, that cannot be, for I am under a spell and cannot leave this place unless someone will cut off the five heads and five necks of the giant; and who can ever do that?"

"Well," the Prince said, "let us ask this clever fellow of a man-servant of mine."

The man-servant said to her to go and tell the giant he was going to fight him, and she did so.

And the giant laughed, "Ho!, ho!" and he laughed, "Hee, hee!" and he rolled with laughing, and took a mighty sword in his hand; but he didn't know that the man-servant was there in his invisible quilt and his shoes of quietness — until he felt a sword flashing about among his five heads; and then he cried, *"Oh, oh!"* instead of, "Ho, ho!" for he couldn't see his opponent. Off went head number one, and off went head number two, and so on, until all five heads were severed from the giant's five necks!

And the fair man-servant placed them on a string and slung them over his shoulder and carried them all to the Prince.

And now the King's son was able to marry the maiden with hair like the raven's wing and cheeks like the raven's blood on the snow; and they stayed on in the giant's house and enjoyed the wealth and the treasure of the three giants, and were very happy.

At the end of a year the fair man-servant came to the Prince and said he must now be leaving him; and the Prince said:

"What reward will you take for all the fine service you have rendered me?"

"What reward will you give me?" said the man-servant.

"Whatever you choose to ask from me, even should you ask my wife herself," said the Prince.

"I will not ask any reward or gift from you," the fair man-servant said, "nor will I ask your wife or your treasures. But do you remember the man whose debts you paid who was lying at the door of the church?"

"I do that," said the Prince.

"Then I am that man, and I came back to earth to pay my debt to you for bringing me to rest. The debt is now paid and I am wishful to return to the place from which I came to you: so fare you well, master, for ever!"

And where he had been standing there was now but a misty cloud! And they never saw the fair man-servant again, but they lived for many years to enjoy the wealth of the giants he had killed.

Gold Tree and Silver Tree

A Highland version of the story of Snow-White, from the island of Eigg

In a western isle there was a King who had a beautiful wife named Silver Tree, and a beautiful daughter named Gold Tree who was betrothed to a Prince on the mainland.

Until Gold Tree grew up, Silver Tree had been the acknowledged beauty of the island kingdom, and now she had become very jealous of her own daughter.

In a glen on the island there was a wise old trout living in a well, and Silver Tree used to go periodically to ask him this question:

"Troutie, bonny little fellow, am I not the most beautiful Queen in the whole world?"

And while Gold Tree was still a little lassie the old trout used to answer her question in the way she wanted, and say, "Yes, Queen, you are."

But after Gold Tree grew up the Queen asked the question and got the answer:

"No, indeed then, you are not."

"Who then, is? asked the Angry Queen.

"Yes, Gold Tree, your daughter, is more beautiful than you."

And this answer turned the Queen so sick with rage and jealousy that she went home and lay down on her bed, and said she would never be well unless she was given the heart of Gold Tree on a silver plate.

At night the King came home from his hunting, and he was told that Silver Tree, the Queen, was very sick; and he went to her and said:

"What is this at all that is ailing you? And what can I do to cure your sickness?"

And the Queen said:

"You can heal my sickness right enough if you will bring me the heart of Gold Tree, my daughter, on a silver plate. Nothing else will cure me."

And to gain time the King said:

"But the Prince has taken her away to be married."

"Then you can send after her and bring her back," said the Queen, and she turned her face to the wall.

Then the King, to satisfy her, sent the lads to the hunting hill for a he-goat, and when it was killed he carried its heart on a silver plate to the Queen, and she rose at once from her bed, cured and well.

A year after this she turned her steps to the glen where the well was in which the old trout lived; and she said:

"Troutie, bonny little fellow, am I not the most beautiful Queen in the world?"

"No, indeed then, you are not."

"No? Who then, is?"

"Yes, Gold Tree, your daughter."

"Gold Tree? No, no! It is long since Gold Tree was living. I got the heart of her on a silver plate a year since!"

"Well, indeed then, I may tell you that she is *not* dead. She is married to a great Prince on the mainland, and it was the heart of a he-goat that you got."

Then Silver Tree went home, and oh, the rage of her!

And she would have the King see that the long-ship was put in order, because she wanted to go and see her dear daughter, Gold Tree, seeing it was long that she hadn't seen her!

And the King was afraid to cross his wife's will, and he got the long-ship put in order for Silver Tree; and she steered the ship herself, and steered so well that they were not long at all in arriving at the part of the mainland where Gold Tree lived.

The Prince was away on the hunting-hill when his mother-in-law came, and Gold Tree was terrified when she saw the long-ship.

"Oh, me!" she said to her old nurse, "my mother is coming here, and she will kill me!"

"Indeed, and she will not get the chance," the nurse said. "We will lock you in a room where she cannot get at you." And it happened as she said.

And when the Queen came to her daughter's Palace and called out, "Where is my dear Gold Tree, my daughter, that she is not coming to see her own mother?" there was no reply to the question.

And then Silver Tree went up to the door of the room where Gold Tree was, and she called out once more:

"If you will not come out, Gold Tree, put your little finger through the keyhole that your mother may kiss it."

And Gold Tree did so, thinking that was safe enough, and when her mother saw the little finger she put a poisoned stab in it, and the poor girl inside the room fell dead!

And the wicked Queen took her way back to the long-ship with her heart full of rejoicing.

When the Prince came home and found his Gold Tree dead, he was drowned in grief for her. And she was still so beautiful that he could not bear to bury her, but he had the body enclosed in glass and laid in a room that was always kept locked; and he always kept the key himself.

After a while he married again, and the new wife got the keys of all the rooms in the house but just the one room where the Prince kept the body of his dear Gold Tree.

Then on a certain day he went away to the hunting and forgot to take the key of that room with him. And when his second wife found the key she went away to see what it was that he was keeping so secret in the locked room.

And what did she see but a most beautiful woman lying enclosed in glass. She lifted the glass lid and touched the lovely hands of her, and then she noticed the stab in the finger and she picked it out; and at once Gold Tree rose, alive, and beautiful as ever!

At fall of night home came the Prince from the hunting-field where all day he had been thinking of his beautiful Gold Tree; and he was very downcast and silent.

His wife remarked on his mood, and said::

"What would you say to me if I could make you smile again?"

"That cannot happen, indeed, unless I should see Gold Tree come to life again," he said sadly.

"Well, at least, come you with me to my room down there, and you will see what you will see," she said.

And, to please her, he followed her to her room, and there he saw his Gold Tree, looking more beautiful than ever! And there were great rejoicings, and he asked what he could do to reward his other wife for the noble part she had played in bringing Gold Tree back to him.

"Indeed, then, I am going away; for Gold Tree is your first and your dearest," she said.

"But, indeed, you *shall not* go away!" Gold Tree said. "Let us all live in peace and happiness together."

And seeing they were all agreed about it, she stayed on.

A while after this, Silver Tree went to the well that was in the glen on the island, and she said to the old trout:

"Troutie, bonny little fellow, am I not the most beautiful Queen in all the world?"

But she got an answer she wasn't expecting:

"No, indeed then, you are not."

"Who, then, is?" she asked in anger.

"Yes, Gold Tree, your daughter."

"But Gold Tree is not living. There is more than a year since I put a poisoned stab in her finger!"

"Oh, indeed, as to that, I cannot say; but she is not dead, I am telling you! She is not dead!"

So Silver Tree went home, and again she demanded that the King would get the long-ship put into order, that she might go again and see her dear daughter, Gold Tree, seeing it was so long since she saw her.

And the King was afraid to refuse her, so the long-ship was put in order, and sailed away; and again the Queen steered the boat herself, and steered so well that they were not long in coming to the part of the mainland where Gold Tree lived.

Again the Prince was out on the hunting-hill, and Gold Tree was frightened when she saw the long-ship coming.

"Oh!" she said to the other wife, "my mother is coming, and she will kill me this time."

"Indeed, then, she will not get the chance," said the other wife. "Come! let us go down to the shore and meet her."

And when Silver Tree came ashore she said to her daughter:

"Gold Tree, love, your mother has brought you a draught

of golden liquid that will give you perpetual happiness. Come and drink it."

But Gold Tree hung back, and the other wife said:

"It is the custom in our country that the one that offers a drink must first take a draught of it herself."

So to please her, Silver Tree put the cup to her lips and made a pretence of drinking from it.

But the other wife got her from behind and forced the poisoned liquid down her throat, and the wicked Queen fell dead.

And they put her body on the ship and sent it sailing away over the waves to wherever the sea would take it; and there, for all I know, it may be sailing still!

And at last Gold Tree was safe, and she and the Prince lived long and happily together, and the other wife was their best friend.

The origin of the fairies

A tale from the ceilidhs of the Western Highlands

Long before the world took shape or form, God was living with his myriads of angels behind thick curtains of mist in the great bright space that is known as Heaven. And because these angels behind the clouds did all things as God willed them, their lives were peaceful, happy, and beautiful. But about the time that God was occupied in creating the world we call the Earth, it happened that there came one into Heaven who introduced a new and evil spirit among the angels there. This was the Spirit of Discontent, which poisoned the minds of certain foolish ones among the angels, so that they followed the Devil — which was the name that was given to the evil one — and became rebellious against God.

Black thoughts grew in the minds of these foolish angels, and darkened their hearts, so that in time their outward appearance was darkened also; and indeed black angels are not good to be looking upon! God was for long patient with these foolish ones, but He feared his good angels might become corrupted by their bad example; so one day he parted the thick curtains of mist that surrounded Heaven — screening it off from the rest of the universe — and He gazed over space.

He saw the stars revolving there below Him, and among them was the newly created earth. Away beyond it, and far below all the stars, He saw a pool of blackness, so vast that the bottom of it could scarcely be fathomed; and in the far distance He saw a red light that gleamed like an eye of fire; so wicked indeed it looked, that the good angels covered their eyes with their wings.

God pointed to the black pool and said to the leading spirit of evil:

"That is where I am putting you and all those rebellious ones of yours, for indeed there is in Heaven no room for them or for yourself. All that blackness is yours for the keeping, and nobody is asking to share it with you at all! And if yourself and your followers should be unhappy there, you needn't be thinking you'll get back into Heaven, for here you would only be trying to poison the minds of my good angels, so now, be going with you!"

God's wrath was so terrible as to shake these evil ones to the very edge of the curtains of mist; but the leading spirit of rebelliousness turned defiantly, and said to his followers:

"Come on, then, with me — you that are on my side." But he gave an evil laugh as he added, "Though God is thinking there's only *good* angels left in Heaven, He'll be finding certain ones that may not be for *me*, it's true, but indeed they are not for Him either, for they are what the people of Earth down there call *Neutrals* — those that take neither one side nor the other!"

But God had no patience with all this talk of the evil one, and He gave him a push, saying, "Now, that's all I'll be listening to from *you*, so be going — you and yours — to yon deep pool of blackness!"

And He gave good-bye to the Spirit of Discontent and dismissed the evil one and his followers — who sank down — down — into the dreadful abyss! And great winds came blowing up from space, winds that cried and groaned as they blew the curtains of mist together; and Heaven was again enveloped, and seemed as peaceful as it used to be. But presently it was found that there was truth in the saying of the evil one about the angels that were neutral; and God thought for long what he would be doing with them. For although they hadn't indeed done any wickedness, it seemed they were not wishful to do any good either; and God was not pleased with them in case they might affect His good angels.

So He called the neutrals together and He said to them:

"There is something I must be telling you. I cannot keep you any longer in Heaven, because you are not with Me -- and those that are not with Me are against Me. That is why I am not keeping you among my good angels any longer. But I am sending you down beyond the curtains of mist, to the world that is called the Earth, and there you are to live under the ground and in the hills as Little People; and the people of the earth will call you *the fairies*. I will not take away the wings from you, and when the moon is full you can come out from your fairy hills and exercise them, in case a time should come when I think you are fit to be recalled to Heaven and you would be needing your wings again."

And that is the way that God dismissed the Neutrals from heaven and put them to live on the Earth as the fairies — or the Little People. For ages and ages they were in their fairy hillocks, with no liberty to come out and show themselves — except at night-time, when mortals used to tell that they had seen them dancing round their fairy rings. But, as time went on, fewer and fewer of the Little People were seen upon the Earth, and it seemed as though they were being taken away somewhere else; for even when the moon was at her brightest they only came in ones and twos, where before they had come in scores. And now the fairy hills are silent, and never a laugh like the tinkle of a fairy bell is heard about the fairy rings, never the flash of a wing, nor an elfish face looking from the cup of a flower!

There are some that blame that on the inventions of Man, and declare that the lighting of darkness by the turn of a switch, the vehicles that run by themselves, and the flash of man-made wings have frightened the fairies away from the Earth. But in the Highlands they have a notion that a long while since — maybe a hundred years or maybe less — God began to be sorry for the fairies having to live under the ground and only getting out at night-time, so that He pardoned tham and took them back to Heaven to give them one more chance!

The origin of music

Told round the peat-fires on Skye

A long time ago there was a widow living in the west of Skye. She was a lonely woman with an only son, and this boy, from the time he was a wee laddie, was different from all the boys in the island.

It seemed as though his thoughts wrapped him round and kept him apart from them all, and he was of a strange melancholy turn of mind.

He would not work on the croft, though indeed an extra pair of hands would have been of value there. All he wanted to do was to wander along by the sea-shore, listening to the sough of the winds and the beat of the waves, and the cry of the seabirds.

One day, when he was wandering along the margin of the surf, something unusual caught his eye among the waves, in the waters of the inflowing tide. "Is it something the waves are trying to hide?" he thought. "No! There it is again! I will wait and see if it will be washed up on the sands!"

The strange thing was borne nearer — and nearer still — and then a wave washed it right up to his feet, and, receding, left it there.

The lad stooped and saw a queer sort of instrument lying on the sands. In growing excitement he picked it up and, as he lifted it, strange sweet sounds filled the air. Timidly he touched the strings of it with his fingers and there issued from it low notes that were music and yet not music, but he knew that if he had but the skill he should be able to take from it music that would move mortals. He carried it tenderly home to his mother, who shrank from it as if afraid.

"Go you back to where you found this thing and put it down in the spot you lifted it from. For it's sure I am this is a fairy instrument the waves have brought to you, and keeping it will only bring you disaster," she said.

But the boy was not wanting to part with his treasure. He kept it beside him day and night, and he would go on touching the strings with his fingers, in the hope that some day he might be given the skill to draw from them music that could be understood of mortals.

But time went on and he found that, although he had the love of music strong in his heart, he had not the skill to express it with his fingers. Then he became more and more melancholy; he wandered continually along the shore, until the people said, "It is hard for his mother that her only son should be out of his mind like this!"

And the mother, distressed to see this lowness of his spirits, went in her trouble to consult a witch doctor, a man well known to have the power to acccomplish many strange things.

The widow asked him would he do one of two things for her boy? Would he either kill the love of music in his heart, or put the skill of music in his fingers, and make him happy?

"I can do that same for you, so that your son will be able to play the harp — which is the name of this instrument — as no other mortal in the Highlands can," the witch doctor replied.

"But if I do, how will you reward me?"

"You know that I am a poor woman, sir," the widow answered, "but I will be willing to pay anything at all, in reason, for my boy's sake, if you will only name your terms."

"Then these are my terms," he said. "I will kill the music in your son's heart if you will promise to deliver yourself over to me at a time that I will state to you. Or I will put the skill of music in his fingers if you will promise to give me your soul when I shall come to claim it. Now choose, woman — choose!"

"I choose that he shall keep the love of music that is in his heart and get the skill of music in his fingers as well," she said, "for my time upon the earth is about spent, and I'll willingly give my soul to make my only son happy!"

Then the master of the black art was pleased, and he said:

"Then you go home, and at a certain time I will come for you that you may fulfil your part of the bargain. You will find when you reach your house that I have fulfilled my part."

And when the widow reached her croft she found it was true what he had told her, for her son had found the skill of music in his fingers, and was drawing beautiful music from his instrument.

"Mother, mother! Listen!" he cried, tremulous with joy. "How has this come to me at all? For when I was feeling the strings and despairing of ever being able to make any music out of them, I suddenly felt the skill flowing to my fingers to make music to match the love of it that has been in my heart."

He was so steeped in joy at his new-found art that he did not notice for some time how sad his mother was becoming. When he did at last notice, it made him first uneasy and then frightened him.

"What is wrong with you, mother? And why is it that you are always looking, and listening, as if you were expecting someone?"

At first she would not tell him, but when at last he

compelled her to share her secret with him and he heard about the bargain she had made with the witch doctor, the lad's distress was terrible. It was in vain for him to offer — as he did at once — to give up his newly acquired skill in order to free her from her bargain. The witch doctor would have none of that, and only insisted that she should hold herself in readiness for his call.

Then it was noticed that as the lad's fingers grew more skilful his music grew in beauty, but it was music of such sadness that no one could listen without tears when he touched the strings of his harp.

And after the master of the black art had taken the mother away to fulfil her part of the bargain, there was that in the lad's music that stilled the birds of the air and brought the fish in the sea to listen to it. And that is why nobody can ever take any but sad music from the harp — which was the origin of music.

PART TWO

By R MacDonald Robertson

(Stories originally edited by Jeremy Bruce-Watt)

This section features stories gathered originally during extensive travels throughout the islands. They are told with true but simple artistry, whether it be that of the old people from whom he collected them, or that of the author himself.

Dunvegan's fairy flag

Every country has its superstitions; and these superstitions have often been interwoven with that country's naval and military glory. This is amply portrayed by the Fairy Flag of the ancient Scandinavians. The Danes had a magical standard called *Roe fans,*or *"Am Fitheach"* (The Raven). It was said to have been embroidered simultaneously by the three daughters of Lodbroke (Loda), and sisters of Hinguar, or Ivar. But within the Castle of Dunvegan in Skye has long been preserved one of these enchanted flags. It came there through the Norwegian ancestry of the Dunvegan family; and some very strange superstitions have been attached to it.

One of these superstitions was, that wherever it was carried into battle, the party which bore it would be victorious — but this end being attained, an invisible being was to carry away both standard and standard-bearer, never more to be seen! The family of Clan-y-Faitter possessed this dangerous office of standard-bearer, and actually held their lands in Braccadale by this singular tenure.

This Fairy Flag of the Macleods has been several times produced. At one time when the family of Dunvegan maintained an unequal combat against Clanranald, the enchanted colours were produced, and, it seems, the Macleods were multiplied tenfold in the eyes of the Clanranalds! The consequence was a victory on the side of Dunvegan. It was brought forward again on a less war-like occasion. The Lady Macleod was pregnant; she longed very much to view the *Bratach Shith,* or Fairy Standard. The charmed flag was produced to save the young heir of Dunvegan.

The flag ensured victory

Duntulm's grim secret

Duntulm Castle, in Skye, was for centuries past the ancient seat of the Lords of the Isles.

On the death of one of the Macdonald chiefs, more than four hundred years ago, a dispute arose among his followers as to who his successor should be. There were two claimants to the honour — the son of the late Chief, arrogant and cruel, and his cousin, a brave and gallant young man who had proved himself a good soldier and leader. Finding themselves in a minority, the cousin and his adherents retired to Uist, where the inhabitants were on their side, to organise a plan for obtaining possession of Duntulm.

There was deep and deadly enmity between the two cousins, for they were rivals in love as well as in war. They were both suitors to the fair Margaret, ward of the late Chief. Under his will, she was to remain at Duntulm until she was of age when two courses were open to her — to marry the young Lord of the Isles or to become a nun. Margaret disliked the idea of being immured in a convent; but at the same time the idea of marriage with the late Chief's son was distasteful to her, as she had already fallen in love with his cousin, who was in the habit of sailing from Uist to Skye under cover of darkness to snatch a few hours in her company in the shadow of the castle walls.

On one such visit, he told her of a plan he had evolved for making himself master of Skye. He proposed to cross the sea at night with all his men, land quietly, then build up with stones every means of exit from the castle, and dig under its foundations until it fell, burying his enemies beneath its crumbling walls. Margaret approved of his scheme, and the lovers separated, full of hope for a speedy reunion.

This hope, alas, was never to be realised. Unseen by them,

the crouching figure of one of the castle retainers had heard every word that was spoken at their secret tryst.

The time appointed for the attack soon arrived — a stormy night when thick clouds obscured the light of the moon, and the sound of distant thunder re-echoed from the rocks. The men embarked with their leader, and battled manfully with the wind and the waves till at length they reached the rocky coast of Skye. They disembarked, and were advancing swiftly and noiselessly when they saw a dark line moving towards them — and the Macdonalds were upon them! The invaders rushed forward to meet their foes, and also to meet their fate. After a short, determined fight, the would-be Chief found himself a prisoner. He was marched under the frowning portals of Duntulm into the presence of his cousin, who received him with mock courtesy, and with pretended apologies for offering him such poor accommodation, led him to the top of the highest turret of the building, and locked him in a tiny room which held only a table on which was a piece of salt beef, a loaf of bread, and a large jug.

For a time the unhappy man gave way to despair; then he began to feel hungry. The beef was very salt, and he soon became thirsty and reached out for the jug. It was empty. He sat for a while stunned and motionless, then he heard voices outside the door of his prison and a strange noise that he could not at first comprehend. As it continued, he understood it too well: it was the sound of masons building up the door of the room, just as he had contemplated building up the door of the castle.

A few months later, the lovely Margaret died heartbroken at a nearby convent. Her lover's ghost was for many years believed to haunt the gloomy Castle of Duntulm, where the death-groans could be heard echoing along the passages. It is said that the castle was abandoned by the Macdonalds about 1715 because the haunting had become so bad.

Many years later, when the turret was again opened, a skeleton was found grasping part of a stone water-jug. The other part had been ground to powder between the teeth of the thirst-maddened prisoner of Duntulm.

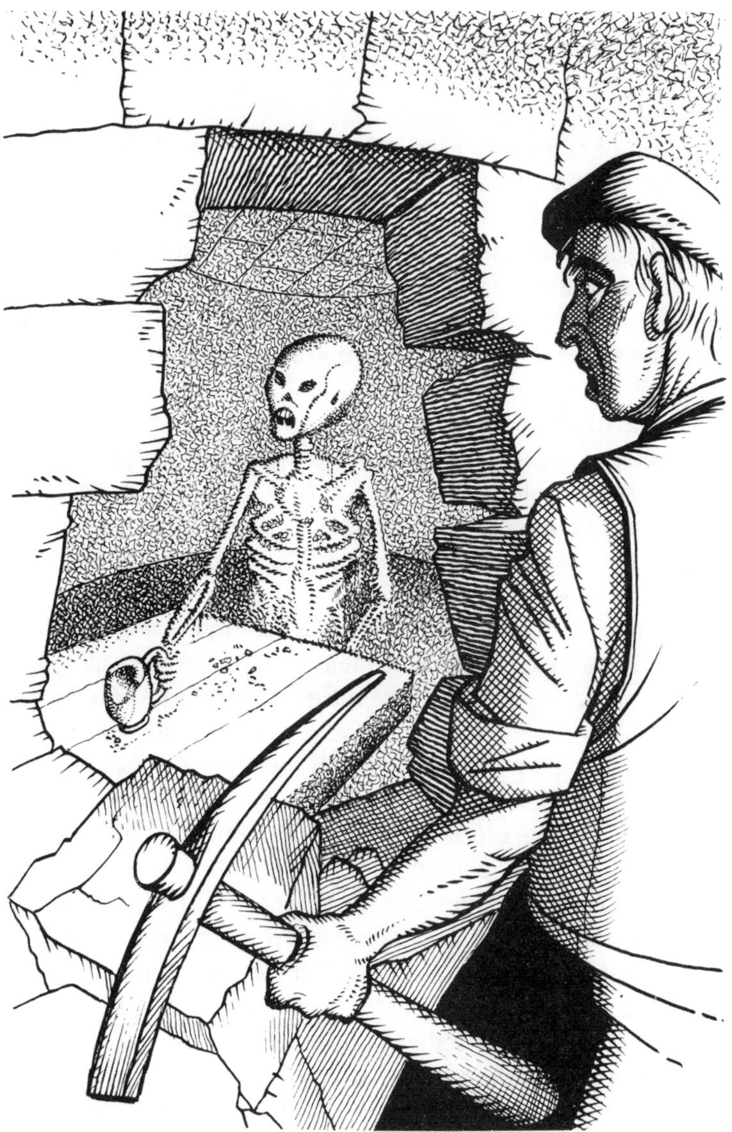

The skeleton was still grasping the stone water jug

Murdered man's revenge

There is a peculiar place on the road between Loch Seaforth and Stornoway in Lewis. There is a rock by the road-side, said to be haunted by the ghost of a boy murdered there many years ago. The legend has it that long ago two Stornoway boys, instead of going to school, amused themselves by egg-collecting during the grouse-hatching season. While amusing themselves stealing eggs, they quarrelled over the division of their spoil. Words turned to blows. One of the lads hit the other over the head with a stone and, although he had not intended to inflict serious injury, killed him outright. When the youth realised the terrible crime that he had committed, he grew frightened, but, keeping his wits about him, dug a hole in the moor under a big rock by the highway by the burnside, in which hole he buried the body of his school companion.

He then went to Harris, boarded a fishing vessel in Tarbert, whence he made his way to the Mainland, became a sailor, and for many years sailed the 'Seven Seas,' wandering about the world. At last, in the course of his voyages, the ship — in which, it is said, he became mate — put in for repairs at Stornoway. When there, instigated by curiosity, he went on shore, only to find no trace of his old homestead, where his own family and that of his poor school-friend once dwelt. New buildings had taken their place. He entered one of these — a small eating and drinking establishment which like others were always open for refreshments to sailors — and called for something to eat.

While his meal was being prepared, his attention was suddenly drawn to something rather peculiar in the shape of the handles of his knife and fork which were lying before him on the table; and he was examining them somewhat minutely, when his hostess addressed him: "Yes, you may well look at those handles, for I got them in a very strange way. I was returning home late one evening from Balallan with a hay-load, and sat down by the burnside at the bottom of the hill near the white rock, when my eyes were attracted by something whitish under the rock. In what seemed to have been a hole in the ground, I found three or four bones of a dead sheep, I assumed, and brought them home with me and had handles made out of some of the bones for two or three of my old knives and forks that required mending, and whose handles had come off and were lost."

The sailor's countenance grew grey. "Hey, my man," said the restaurant owner, "what's the matter with your hands? They are all smeared with blood!"

As the sailor felt the bone-handles turn in his grasp, and seem to move and wriggle in his hands, he sprang to his feet with a wild scream, and yelled: "They're not sheep's bones at all; they're poor Willie's bones and I murdered him: they witness against me!" It was not the sailor's hands but the bones which oozed blood. Thereupon he confessed to his crime, and was afterwards tried, found guilty,condemned, and finally executed on the Gallows Hill, protesting to the very last that he never had any ill-will towards his school-friend, but that he had only killed poor Willie in a fit of passion, and had regretted his deed bitterly, ever since.

Ever since, the big white rock has been haunted — but the spectre has never been seen on the way to, but always on the way back from Stornoway. The stone is situated about four miles from Soval, on the right-hand side of the highway, at the bottom of a hill, by a little stream. As you walk down the road from Soval you see nothing of the rock from Stornoway. To this day, it is said, the sailor's ghost haunts the Gallows Hill, as well.

The Blue Men of the Minch

The "Blue Men" have been seen only in the Minch, and chiefly in the strait which separates Lewis from the *"Shiant Isles"* (charmed islands). The Sound is called after them *"Sruth nam Fear Gorm"* (Sound of the Blue Men). They are said to be of human size and of great strength. Night and day they swim round and round and between the Shiant Isles, and that is why the sea there is never at rest. They have been described as blue-coloured, with long grey faces that they raise with their long restless arms above the waves.

"Sruth nam Fear Gorm" has often been called "The Current of Destruction" because so many ships have been swamped there. Sailors were afraid of the Blue Men, who were said to take a mad delight in attacking ships; and many sailed round the Shiant Isles instead of taking the short cut bewteen them and the Island of Lewis.

A ship is once said to have come upon a blue-coloured man asleep on the waters. He was taken aboard and bound hand and foot till it was impossible for him to get away. The ship had not gone far when two Blue Men bobbed up above the water and shouted:—

"Duncan will be one, Donald will be two;
Will you need another ere you reach the shore?"

On hearing this, the captive snapped the ropes that bound him as if they had been made of straw, and leapt out of the boat into the sea.

There is a boatman's song about the Blue Men, the last verse of which runs:—

The Blue Men of the Minch took a delight in attacking ships

"Oh, weary on the Blue Men, their anger and their
wiles!
The whole day long, the whole night long, they're
splashing round the isles;
They'll follow every fisher — ah! they'll haunt the
fisher's dream —
Where billows toss, oh, who would cross the Blue
Men's stream?"

According to West Sutherland fishermen, the Blue Men are said to enjoy following steamers and other water craft on their way to and from Stornoway. They swim in groups or gangs and rise up above their waists in the water to attract attention. They are of a glossy-blue appearance and are distinguished from the mermaids on account of their bearded faces. They use their teeth as well as their legs and arms in battle. Some say that their appearance generally foretells stormy weather.

The mermaid and the Lord of Colonsay

Many years ago, there lived on the island of Colonsay a young chieftain renowned for his prowess in battle. He was betrothed to a beautiful lady whom he loved dearly, and their wedding-day had been fixed, when a message came across the sea from the King of Scotland asking the Lord of Colonsay to help him drive off a horde of fierce invaders threatening to take his kingdom.

The chieftain ordered his ship to be made ready, and went to bid farewell to his lady. She gave him a ruby ring, telling him to wear it always for her sake. "'As long as my heart is yours," she said, "the jewel will glow with blood-red fire." He then set off for the wars.

She gave him a ruby ring to wear always

On reaching the mainland, he fought with the King against his enemies, and overcame them. Once more he set sail for his native isle.

The sea was calm and the rowers strong, and when daylight had faded and the moon was casting its silvery beams over the water, the boat was in sight of the island.

Full of joy at the prospect of meeting his lady so soon, the young chieftain could not sleep; but paced the deck, looking out across the waves to the land ahead.

Suddenly he saw, reclining on the crest of a wave, a most beautiful maiden, with golden hair reaching to her waist, and great blue eyes. Thinking she must have fallen overboard from some other ship, he called to the crew to cease rowing. But they either would not, or could not obey him; and the boat sped swiftly on. Then the Lord of Colonsay remembered all he had heard of the merfolk who dwelt in the caves of the ocean, and a shudder crept over him at the thought that he was looking on one of their number. His affection was fixed on the lady he had left on Colonsay, and he had no desire to be tempted by a mermaid's siren wiles. He drew back, but as the boat swept past, the sea-maiden stretched out a white hand and seizing the unfortunate man round the waist, dived down with him into the depths of the sea.

The boatmen, who had seen nothing of this, soon missed their master, and came to the conclusion that he had fallen overboard; and carried back this sad news to the people of Colonsay. They mourned him as dead, but his lady held to the belief that he would one day return alive and well.

Meanwhile, the young chieftain had been carried down through the ocean by his captor. Green and purple distances were above him, and green and purple distances below. He saw the sea-monsters heaving past, and the hulks of wrecked ships, and the bones of drowned mariners; and further down, where gloom gave way to gloom, vast livid tangles of seaweed that coiled and writhed like living things. At last she brought him to a wonderful region at the bottom of the sea, where the floor was yellow sand and the roof was the dark blue ocean. Here there were hundreds of caves, all opening out of each other, and the sand was covered with pink coral, and mother-of-pearl; and there were jewels, and cups and plates of gold and silver half-buried in it, that had been taken from the holds of wrecked treasure-ships.

Here the sea-maiden tried by all her wiles to persuade the chieftain to stay, leaning over him so that he could feel the softness of her yellow hair, and could gaze into the depths of her blue eyes. She spoke to him, and her voice was low and honey-sweet. But he spurned all her advances, and springing to his feet, demanded to be taken back at once to the land above the sea.

"Think better of it," cried the mermaid. "If you will not stay with me willingly, I shall place you in a cave, the entrance to which is barred by the sea, and there you shall remain for ever, and your lady will waste her life waiting for your return. Think better of it, and give me your love."

"Never," replied the young chieftain, declaring that he would rather die than be false.

As he spoke, the pink coral and the yellow sand, and the treasure-trove vanished from sight; and he saw in front of him only a black, gaping hole, across which the waves dashed, barring any exit. The mermaid plunged through the hole into the sea, lashing the water to fury with her tail.

The chieftain was left alone to mourn his fate and to sigh for his island home and his lady. He often looked at the ruby ring on his finger and saw that it still glowed brightly, and he knew by that that his lady had remained faithful to him. The sight of the blood-red stone always gave him renewed courage.

One day the mermaid swam into the cave, looking more beautiful than ever, with a jewelled comb holding back her golden hair. She spoke gently to him, and promised to let him go if he would grant her one favour.

When he asked her what she wanted, she replied, "your

ruby ring." She had of course no intention of letting him go if he gave it to her, but knew that once she had it in her possession, she could find a way to send it to the lady as a proof of her lover's death. Then, she reasoned, the lady would wed someone else, and the knight, believing that she had been unfaithful, would lose all interest in her, and would be content to dwell for ever under the sea.

But the chieftain saw a chance of escape if he promised to grant her request. He said that he would gladly give her the ring if she would do him a favour in return. "Carry me once more to the surface of the sea," he said, "and let me look for the last time on my beloved island. Then I will give you the ring."

She bore him upwards through the water to where the stars looked down on Colonsay, then held out her hand for the ring. The chieftain slipped from her grasp and gave a mighty spring on to a ledge of smooth rock that ran out from the shore.

Mad with rage and disappointment at having been outwitted by a mortal, the mermaid dived from sight beneath the waves. The people of Colonsay believe to this day that when they sail over the spot where she disappeared, they can hear the wild lament which she sighs for ever under the sea for the chieftain whom she loved and lost.

Donald Black and "The Terror"

A man of the village of Caolas, in Tiree, Domhnull Mac an Duibh (Donald Black) was married for the fourth time. His corn was being kiln-dried and he was sitting up one night in the solitary hut where the kiln was kept, blowing on the fire to keep it alive, when the figure of his first wife appeared, and told him to beware, for "*ant-eagal*" (The Terror) was coming; it was at "*crudhan eich*" (The Horseshoe) — a landmark on the public road to Caolas, about a mile and a half away.

She warned the terror was coming

The heat of the fire made him drowsy, and Donald was dozing off to sleep when the figure of his second wife appeared, crying that The Terror was drawing near; it was at "*Cachlaidh na Cuil Connaidh*" (Gateway of the Fuel Enclosure). Disregarding this warning also, he was once more dropping off to sleep when another apparition appeared before him. This was his third wife, who said that The Terror was now at "*Bail uach-drach*" (the upper village).

This warning struck home, and Donald left the kiln with all speed and made for his cottage. He had hardly got into bed when the whole house was shaken as if by an earthquake. A violent wind-storm, the like of which had never before been known in Tiree, swept past the windows, carrying garden palings and all before it. The gale raged all night, but the house stood firm and its occupants were unharmed.

A dead man shot by an arrow

Martin, the historian of the Western Isles, records the following instance of Second Sight, as related to him by Sir Norman MacLeod of Berneray:—

There was a man in Harris who was always being seen by those with Second Sight with an arrow in his thigh, and the islanders believed he would meet his death by being shot in some conflict. In course of time, however, the man died a natural death.

An arrow pierced the thigh

His body was brought up for burial to St Clement's Church, at Rodil; and at the same time another funeral party arrived, with another body to be buried in the same church. An argument arose as to which party should enter the church first. A general melee followed, and someone let fly several arrows.

When Sir Norman MacLeod of Berneray, who was present, at last succeeded in persuading them to stop, it was discovered that an arrow had pierced the thigh of the dead man as he lay on the bier, waiting for burial. Thus were the Seer's predictions fulfilled.

A Benbecula seer

I was staying with a friend at Creagorry, on the Island of Benbecula and was fishing a loch called Langivat. There is a church at one end of the loch, and my gillie said to me: "This is the loch where the minister's son was drowned some years ago. That is his father's church and manse." It appeared that the boy had been playing on the banks of the loch with friends, and had fallen into the water. The other children at once ran to the manse and told his father, who came with help. By that time the boy had disappeared and they were unable to find the body.

He arrived at the loch with his instrument for digging kelp

A member of the father's congregation was digging kelp on South Uist (the neighbouring island to Benbecula) when he suddenly stopped and thought: "The minister's son has been drowned in Loch Langivat and they cannot find him. I see the body and I will go over at once." He arrived at the loch with his long-handled pronged instrument for digging kelp. He at once went and found the body of the minister's son and pulled it out.

I said to the gillie: "Is this true? It sounds ridiculous to me." He replied that the man was still alive. I was duly introduced to him, and asked him what it was that had made him go over to the loch. All he said was, "I don't know why I went. I just had an impulse and felt compelled to go."

A Harris woman's baking

Told by Mr George Ross, Corriemulzie, Sutherland

A Harris woman was walking along the sea-shore when, on passing a rock, she noticed an opening in its side, leading into a spacious cavern. A *Beanshith* (fairy woman) was standing by the opening dressed in green and invited the woman to accompany her and visit a sick person inside the cave.

Although the woman thought the invitation a strange one, she duly accepted and entered, and found herself surrounded by a large company of "little people" for whom she was ordered to begin baking. She was handed only a small quantity of meal, but was confidently asssured that when this was exhausted she would be allowed to go in peace. But the more she baked, the more meal there seemed to be in the barrel. Day after day she toiled to finish her baking, but each evening found her no nearer the end of her task than when she had begun.

One day the entire fairy company left the cave. It was the first time the woman had been left alone, and she paused from her irksome task to examine her prison more closely.

As she moved towards the innermost recess, she heard a moaning cry, which came from an incredibly old man lying on a bed of straw on the stone floor. "What brings you here?" he asked. She told him how she had been lured into the cavern to attend to a sick person, and had instead been set to work on the task of baking which seemed never ending.

"Begin once again," counselled the old man, "but this time stop putting the dusting-meal back amongst your baking."

She carried out his instructions, and in no time the meal was used up and she was able to quit the cave before the inhabitants returned.

The more she baked, the more meal there seemed to be in the barrel

The mermaid's grave

Included by the courtesy of Sir Arthur Waugh, past-President of The Folk-Lore Society

"My story of an encounter with a mermaid at close quarters comes from the little island of Benbecula in the Hebrides.

Somewhere about 1830, the islanders were cutting seaweed or "kelp," a fertilizer, on the shore when one of the women went to wash her feet at the lower end of a reef. The sea was calm, and a splash made the woman look up, and out to sea. What she saw caused her to cry out, and the rest of the party, hurrying to her, were astonished at the sight of a creature 'in the form of a maiden in miniature' some few feet away in the sea.

The little sea-maiden, unperturbed by her audience, played happily, turning somersaults and otherwise disporting herself. Several men waded out into the water and tried to capture her, but she swam easily beyond their grasp. Then a wretched little boy threw stones at her, one of which struck her on the back.

She was next heard of a few days later, but, alas, then she was dead; her body was washed ashore, about two miles from where she was first seen. A detailed examination followed, and we learn that 'the upper part of the creature was about the size of a well-fed child of three or four years of age, with an abnormally developed breast. The hair was long, dark and glossy, while the skin was white, soft and tender. The lower part of the body was like a salmon, but without scales.'

The lifeless body of the little mermaid attracted crowds to the beach where she lay, and the Highland spectators were convinced that they had gazed upon a mermaid at last.

But the story does not end here. Mr Duncan Shaw, Factor (Land Agent) for Clanranald, baron-bailie and sheriff of the district, after seeing the corpse, gave orders that a coffin and shroud be made for the mermaid, and, in the presence of many people, she was buried a little distance above the shore where she was found. The Factor was unlikely to be credulous, and that he ordered a coffin and shroud for the strange little creature cast upon his shores suggests that he thought she was at least partly human."

ALEXANDER CARMICHAEL, *Carmina Gadelica.*

Actually, the alleged mermaid was interred in the presence of a large assemblage of the Hebridean people in the burial-ground at Nunton, where her grave is pointed out to this day. I have seen it myself.

R.M.R.

The spirit multitude

The West Wind was believed to bring in its train the "sluagh" (spirit multitude) which descended on the Western Highlands and the Hebrides from time to time. Few have seen the spirit host that follows in the wake of the West Wind; but on clear frosty nights many have heard their conflicts in the sky — the shouting of combatants and the clashing of their armour.

The "sluagh" was believed to consist of the spirits of men, and it was said to hover over the places where the individuals composing it had transgressed when in human form. This aerial army might easily invade a dwelling house unobserved, though every precaution was taken against them. They often come down to earth; and when the night is dark and the sea roars with anger on the rocks, the people of Barra and South Uist declare that the "sluagh" is seeking shelter in the grasses by the shore; and queer tales are still told in Benbecula of human beings carried off by the spirit host.

Wild swans

Wild swans are called in the North "the enchanted sons of kings." They swim in the shape of white birds on the waterways and fly across the northern sky; and are believed to lament as they go:—

"There is nothing anywhere for us now but brown earth and drifting clouds and wan waters. Why should we not go from place to place as the wind blows, and see each day new fields of reeds, new forest trees, new mountains? Oh, we shall never see the star-heart of any mountain again!"

It is said that the watcher by the shores of the firth or by the lonely mountain tarn may see the wild swans taking off their *"cochull"* (coverings) and resuming their proper shape as men in their endeavours to free themselves from the spell they are under. This however is impossible until three times three hundred years have passed.

Funeral customs and the omens of death

Three knocks at regular intervals of one or two minutes might be heard in any part of the dwelling-house, on the entrance door, on a table, on a window, or even on the top of a "bun-bed." The sounds were quite different from any other — dull and heavy — something eerie about them. A similar omen was the "dead-drap." Its sound resembled that of a continued drop of water falling slowly and regularly from a height; but it was leaden and hollow. Night was the usual time when they were heard. They were audible first by one person, and could not be heard by a second without taking hold of the one that first heard them. This was the case with all the sights and sounds that prognosticated death, and lasted for any length of time. Phenomena like these were universally admitted in the Highlands and Islands of Scotland.

Before the death of a member of the household, there was at times heard during the hours of darkness, the noise as if something heavy were being laid down outside the door of the dwelling-house — the noise of the coffin outside, before it was taken inside the house. A murmur of many voices was occasionally overheard about the front door — the harbinger of the conversation of those who were to assemble for the funeral.

The fairies and the MacCrimmons of Skye

Sometimes the fairies communicate their musical skill to mortal favourites. To them has been ascribed the excellence in music of the MacCrimmons, for centuries pipers to the Macleods.

"An Gille Dubh Macruimein" (the Black Lad MacCrimmon) was the youngest of three sons, and the least thought of by his father. One day, his father and brothers went to a fair, and he was left at home alone. When they had gone, "An Gille Dubh" took down the chanter and began to play on it. He walked out-of-doors as he played, and wandered on till he came to the dwelling of "Beanshith Uaimh an Oir" (the Fairy Woman of the Cave of Gold), which he entered. She handed him a silver chanter on which she gave him a lesson. Then she told him to think of any tune he pleased and play it in the way she had shown him. He did so, and played the tune skilfully. Then the fairy woman said to The Black Lad, "A nis is tu Righ nam Piobairean. Cha robh do leithid romhad, agus cha bhi do leithid as do dheidh" (Now thou art the King of Pipers. Thine equal was not before thee, and thine equal shall not be after thee). So saying, she disappeared.

The clutching hand

An Lamh Shanntach

A young lady, touring the Outer Hebrides, was making her way due south from Barvas (in Lewis) to Harris when she lost her way in the grey Atlantic mist and sought sanctuary in a remote cottage near Leverborough.

After supper with the crofter and his wife, she retired to her room. Something made her feel uneasy. The piteous howling of a dog mingled with the shriek of the night wind. She crossed to the window and closed it firmly, and bolted the door; but even then she did not feel safe. The candle was casting shadows on ceiling and floor; and she became aware of a curious musty odour in the room as of something long since dead. She lost no time in getting into bed, where, tired out, she soon fell asleep.

She was suddenly awakened by the loud moaning of the wind. There was a crash at the window, followed by the sound of broken glass falling on the floor. The window-blind billowed out into the room, and seemed to bring something with it — what, she did not know; but she realised that she was no longer alone. The smell of putrefaction was so strong she had difficulty in breathing. Once more the whines of a dog sounded from outside.

When she regained consciousness, she became aware of a cold, clammy hand that gripped her ankle with fingers of steel. Too terrified to move, she felt the hand travel to her throat. With a desperate courage born of the conviction that her last hour had come, she seized the hand, to find that it was attached to a sinewy arm that ended in space — there was no body at the end of it! Once more she fell back unconscious on her pillow.

Unconsciousness passed into healthy slumber, and she slept peacefully until morning. When she awoke she would have dismissed the episode of the clutching hand as a hideous dream, had not the broken window-pane remained as mute evidence that something other than the wind had entered her room the night before. When she recounted her horrible experience to her host at breakfast, he told her the following story:—

Many years before, an old bed-ridden woman lay dying in a four-poster bed in an upstairs room in the cottage, where she lived alone.

She had confided in her doctor that she had hidden all her worldly wealth — a bag full of golden coins — in the mattress of the bed on which she lay; and he, pretending to attend her, had slipped his hand under the bedclothes in order to secure the prize. As he did so, however, the dying woman started up from her coma. With her last breath she cursed the doctor in a flood of vituperative Gaelic — the gist of which was that his clutching arm should never find peace in the grave but should remain "earthbound" till the Day of Judgment!

The room in which the old woman had died became a "haunted room" once a year — on each anniversary of her death — when anyone who had the misfortune to sleep in it experienced the phenomenon of "The Clutching Hand."

In the excitement of welcoming an unexpected visitor, the crofter and his wife had quite forgotten the date, and had unwittingly sent their guest to sleep in the haunted room. They apologised profusely for their thoughtlessness.

According to local tradition, the doctor was the only one present at the old woman's death-bed. As she breathed her last, he drew the curtains round her. Her friends ordered the coffin to be sent to the house, and it was delivered by the local joiner (with whom the doctor was in league). When the mourners arrived on the day of the funeral, they found the box already closed down.

The bearers were heard to remark that the old woman

must have wasted a lot in her last illness, as the coffin was so light; but it was duly interred with full religious rites. Only on returning to the cottage did they discover that the corpse was still in the curtained bed!

This necessitated another funeral — with another coffin — the following day; and this time her friends actually saw the old woman's remains placed in the box.

It was widely rumoured that the doctor, not daring to be seen leaving the cottage with the gold, had with the help of his accomplice smuggled it out in the first coffin, and later removed it from the grave.

Whatever may have been the truth of this story — believed to have emanated from the disgruntled joiner — the doctor disappeared the day after the funeral, and the gold with him. Neither was ever seen again.

A cure for the "Evil Eye"

A cure for the "Evil Eye," as practised in Uist, is as follows:

The person first goes for water, and, if possible, it is taken from a burn across which the living pass, and over which the dead are carried. Having brought the water into the house, he repeats the Paidir (pater) and the Creud (credo). He then takes the coin or coins (the more valuable the more potency) and, in the name of Father, Son and Holy Ghost, puts it or them into the water. Thereafter three palmfuls (tri boiseagan) are sprinkled in the name of the Trinity on the person or animal suffering.

The performer then goes with the dish of water to the fireside, and sprinkles three handfuls on the fire, repeating these words:—

"Will fire burn envy?
Fire will burn envy."

The remainder of the water is then taken outside, and spilled on a flag or rock — that is, a flag or rock *in situ.* If, after the water is spilled out, and the vessel turned upside down, one or other of the coins adhere to the vessel, always a wooden one, and generally the broth-pot ladle, it is considered proof positive of the need for, and also of the efficacy of, the enchantment.

Paul of the Thong

Nine miles from Portree in Skye a road branches to Kingsburgh where the mansion stood in which Prince Charles was harboured, and where Dr Johnson met Flora Macdonald. No vestige of the house remains, but a few stunted trees mark its site. A short distance farther you enter that part of Trodda-nish which belonged to Angus or Aonghas Fionn, who figures prominently in Gaelic history as having slain the murderer of Donald Hearrach. The incident is worth mentioning, on account of the curious manner in which Donald was killed.

The story runs that he was invited to a feast at which, among other pastimes, leaping was proposed, it being known that Donald's agility would carry the palm of victory. Accordingly, a leathern thong with a running loop was prepared, the loop being suspended over the place where Donald was to leap, while the other end of the thong was held in an adjoining apartment. Donald, unconscious of the trap, leaped his highest, and at the moment that his head was within the noose the cord was tightened with savage determination, and he was strangled. The perpetrator of this deed went afterwards by the soubriquet, Pol na h-Eill, or Paul of the Thong, and he it was whom Angus killed.

The Monster of Sleat

A great sea serpent was said to haunt the Sound of Sleat between the Isle of Skye and the mainland, and was said to have been seen by Mr Maclain, a minister who lived in the district in the nineteenth century. Mr Maclain, who owned a small yacht, went sailing in the Sound, and one day put out to sea with some friends. The huge sea-serpent suddenly reared its head above the water quite close to the yacht, and caused such a wave that it nearly capsized the boat. It was said to resemble a gigantic eel and its girth was like that of a fish-barrel.

With the serpent wriggling nearby, Mr Maclain headed his yacht down the Sound and sailed into the safety of Loch Hourn, which lay to the south. The beast was said to resemble the Loch Oich monster, which Mr A J Richards of London claimed to have seen in 1936. He was boating on the south-western end of the loch when he heard a commotion in the water nearby. Parts of a huge snake-like body rose to the surface, then the head appeared about a yard in front of the humps. The head was said to resemble that of a dog, and the colouring of the monster was black.

PART THREE

By Francis Thompson

In this section the highly respected Stornoway based writer Francis Thompson reflects on Second Sight and the festivals and customs that marked time through the year.

Second sight — back from the dead

The Gaelic word for second sight is *da-shealladh,* which means 'two sights', perhaps conveying the idea that a vision of the world of sense is one sight, but a vision of another world, populated by people living but not within actual sight of the seer, or living in another time, is another, rarer, sight.

Through the faculty of his gift, the seer can 'see' the dead returned to earth, revisiting the physical world for some purpose, and he can also see wraiths, fetches, doubles or apparitions of the living, either in the present time, or in a future time.

Visions seem to fall into two general categories: those which involve living people, contemporary with the seer, and often with his or her close friends or relations, who appear as wraiths, and might be taken as 'precognition' — the ability to foretell events about to happen, and which do occur within a short time of the forecast.

The other category contains visions of events which often involve those not yet born and which are more difficult to explain in contemporary language, images and meanings, and also to establish their actual time.

The latter sights are contained in the visions of the true seer: the person able to project far into the future and, though he or she has no means of knowing whether the vision will come to pass, are sufficiently convinced of their gift that the details of the vision are set down and recorded.

Island Experiences

Some of the the first such recorded instances of second sight and seers occur in the book written towards the end of the 17th century by Martin Martin. He quotes some thirty cases, most of them of Skye origin.

He defines second sight as "a singular Faculty of Seeing an otherwise invisible Object, without any previous Means us'd by the Person that sees it for that end; the Vision makes such a lively impression upon the Seers, that they neither see nor think of anything else, except the Vision, as long as it continues: and then they appear pensive or jovial, according to the Object which was represented to them."

It is interesting to note that Martin, who was antagonistic towards all superstitions which offended his religious convictions, was, however, firmly convinced of the existence of second sight, and even went some way to answer the objections of sceptics.

From Martin's time there grew an interest in the subject, to be developed by such men as Samuel Pepys, the Revd Robert Kirk of Aberfoyle, John Aubrey, Dr Samuel Johnson and Sir Walter Scott.

The Swiss scientist, Necker de Saussure, and that indefatigable tourist, Thomas Pennant, both mention one of the most famous instances of second sight: Lord President Forbes foretelling, at the time of the Battle of Prestonpans (1745), that the Jacobite Rising would end disastrously at Culloden (April 1746).

Among the instances of second sight quoted by Martin is one which he himself heard fully eighteen months before the event took place. The vision concerned a seer on the island of

Eigg "who frequently saw an apparition of a man in a red coat lined with blue, and having on his head a strange sort of blue cap with a very high cock on the fore part of it, and that the man who there appeared was kissing a comely maid in the village wherein the seer dwelt."

About a year and a half later, a Major Ferguson landed on the island with 600 men to reduce the islanders who had been 'out' for King James.

The soldiers wreaked their vengeance on the islanders. The Major wore exactly the same clothing as predicted by the seer.

In 1703, four years after the appearance of Martin Martin's book, the Rev John Frazer, Minister of Tiree and Coll, wrote about his encounters with second sight and quoted many instances of the gift as it appeared in the Inner Hebrides.

Frazer went a bit farther than Martin; rather than accepting the gift as a natural extension of the human mind, he tried to explain it in the context of the ideas of his day, in terms of images coming from things, passing into the brain through eye and ear, and there stored up in order in its various compartments.

He accounts for visions — sounds being seen and heard — on the principle of the present day recording by electronic means which allows for playback of sound and vision by videotape, the brain being the facility for Frazer's 'replay'.

This solution is possibly near the mark, in that it takes in the idea of time-warping, allowing future events to appear as contemporary happenings.

However, when Frazer came to sticky patches, he referred the matter as an example of the direct will of God, since he was satisfied that the visions were sent for the edification of believers.

Another writer, a Minister on Skye named Macpherson, wrote about second sight in 1763. He, it seemed, had travelled extensively throughout the Highlands and Islands and uncovered so much on second sight that he felt impelled to record his experiences.

He accounts for the gift as being based on certain physical and mental disorders.

Seers, he said, were possessors of minds 'of a melancholy cast' and 'in some instances they are weak-sighted'.

His theory aligns with that which supposes genius to be the product of disease. He stressed the fact that the stories he quoted were given to him on the authority of the narrators: "persons of undoubted veracity who had no interest or design to falsify or disguise the truth of their narrations."

One story concerned Donald MacKinnon, an 'honest tenant' in Skye. In the harvest time of 1760, in the dusk of the evening, as he was binding corn in his field, he suddenly saw a neighbour of his followed by a number of people carrying a corpse and walking right through his other field of standing corn.

Naturally he was not pleased at the destruction of his crop. But there was something uncanny about what he saw. For instance there was no sound.

He immediately went home and told his wife; both went out to inspect the damage and found nothing; not even a stalk of corn had been trampled down.

A year later, he saw his neighbour, accompanied by others, carrying a corpse, walking through the same field on the way to the burial ground at Trumpan.

The Marking of Time

The reflection of a people's beliefs, their attitudes to ancient traditions, and their stance on matters affecting individuals in a community, or the community as a whole, is to be found in no surer mirror than in the calendar of events kept throughout the whole year.

The twelvemonth cyclic period in human lives, with its four internal changes, is the hook onto which is hung the old clothes of one's ancestors, kept up to date by shifts in emphasis as the community's history is altered by internal and external influences and events.

Many of the 'days' kept in Scotland are now forgotten.

But documentary records and oral tradition show that there was once an intense interest in their observance, for one reason or another, but not least to obtain the propitiation of some saint, or revered historical or mythological figure, for the welfare of the future.

The following short tour through calendar observances reveals the substance of the lore of Highland folk.

The time of Lent was 'Am Traisg', the time of fasting.

This was an important date in the calendar for a number of reasons.

In past years, time was counted by church festivals, the priest being the time-keeper for his parish; there was a calendar at the beginning of his service-book, and so the community came to him for their chronology.

In many parts of the Highlands which remained Catholic long after the Reformation, the socket of the Pastoral Candle, and even the candle itself, was used to advertise the approach of significant times; this reckoning succeeded the older folk-reckoning which was based on the same luminary, the moon.

One Gaelic mode of calculation was "Seven short weeks from Shrove-tide to Easter."

When the full moon of Shrove-tide came a few days after St Bride's Day, it was known as a time thought to bring evil to any greedy person.

It was, too, a time for prognostication; for nut-burning and marriage divination, for putting symbolic articles in brose and on cakes specially prepared for the occasion.

In the Highlands matrimonial brose was a savoury dish generally made from the bree of a fat jigget of beef or mutton. Before the bree was served on a plate, a ring was mixed in with the meal, which it was the aim of each eater to win.

After the brose came bannocks, enough to satisfy all the young people present at the feasting and with sufficient symbols shared out to make all happy.

In baking the bannocks the baker had to remain silent until they were cooked; one word could destroy the divination properties of the whole batch.

One cake was given to each person, who then slipped off to bed quietly with it; sleeping with one's head on the bannock could provide one with the sight of a future partner in a dream.

The sun was believed to dance at its rising on the sixth Sunday in Lent, which is Palm Sunday.

On that morning, it was the custom for people in the Hebrides to go to the top of a hill or rising ground to catch a sight of the sun as it came above the horizon.

The Sunday before Easter was the 'Day of the Big Porridge'.

As this day fell at a period late in Spring, and particularly if the winter's winds had failed to cast up a sufficient supply of seaware on the shores, it was time to resort to extraordinary means to secure the necessary manure for the land in some parts of the Outer Hebrides.

A large pot of porridge was prepared with butter and other good ingredients, and then taken to the headlands near creeks, where seaweed was normally to be found.

A quantity of this 'brochan' was then poured into the sea from each headland, accompanied by certain incantations and in consequence of which acts, it was believed, the harbours became full of seaware thrown up by the sea.

Good Friday was of particular significance in the lives of island folk.

Many taboos were recognised.

No iron, for instance, had to come into contact with the ground.

It was expressly forbidden to plough on Good Friday, though potatoes could be planted with a wooden dibble, and the ground raked over with a wooden-toothed rake.

So great was the aversion to doing any ploughing that there was, in some areas, a permanent prohibition on every Friday.

If a burial had to take place, the grave had to be opened the previous day and the earth settled over the coffin with a wooden shovel.

No blacksmith could work on Good Friday, because the nails of the Cross were said to have been made on that day.

It was a popular belief that those born on Good Friday had the power of seeing spirits and of commanding them.

The festival of Beltane, the Fire Festival, was of special importance, particularly in its connections with what was once popularly called 'fire worship.'

The celebration of Beltane on the first day of May was significant as being a good time for the propitiation of the elements, particularly the sun, to influence the growing crops.

Cattle were made to pass through the smoke of the Beltane fires so that they might be cleansed of any evil spirits which might bring them disease during the ensuing year.

In the Highlands, the 'Taine Eigin', the fire of need, was lit on this day (after all the fires in the community had been extinguished) and from its new flames all house fires in the community were re-lit.

Rowan tree and red thread

Deeply embedded in this festival was the belief that at this time, the welcoming of summer, there was a grand anniversary review of all witches, warlocks, fairies, wizards and other spirits and spirit controllers, to which new entrants were admitted.

Such a congregation of evil was much to be feared and it was thus essential that every ritual was carried out in the right manner to ward off any ill effects from the annual convention of evil; rowan twigs, tied with red thread and made into crosses, were inserted into door lintels; and Beltane bannocks were baked and distributed to the children.

Beltane bannocks were made like oatcakes, in the usual way, but washed over with a thin batter of whipped egg, milk and cream, and a little oatmeal.

The Beltane bannock was still being baked as late as the turn of this century in Lewis.

Like its counterpart in the Celtic year, Samhainn, in November, the origin of Beltane cannot be traced to ecclesiastical sources.

Like the names for February (the storm month) and July (the hot month) they predate Christianity.

Beltane was essentially the opening day of the year, when the rigours of winter were finally cleared away and the months ahead showed promise of warmth and fertility.

Its arrival signalled a wide range of activities such as releasing the cattle for their trek to the summer pastures among the hills.

A churning of butter was necessary, as was the making of a